Dear Kate ~

Congratulations on your
First Holy Communion !!!
I saw this Book and thought
of you ~ I hope you enjoy it !!!
God's Blessings to you, always ~

Love,
Dr. Bee

What Angels See

Written by Matthew Kilmurry

Illustrated by Tammie Lyon

Pauline
BOOKS & MEDIA
Boston

Library of Congress Control Number: 2020932789

CIP data is available.

ISBN 10: 0–8198–8381–6
ISBN 13: 978–0-8198–8381–0

Design by Mary Joseph Peterson, FSP
Illustrated by Tammie Lyon

Prayer of Thanksgiving for the Eucharist contributed by Christina M. Wegendt, FSP

Published by Pauline Books & Media, 50 Saint Paul's Avenue, Boston, MA 02130–3491

Printed in the USA

WAS SIPSKOGUNKYO5-24081 8381-6

www.pauline.org

Pauline Books & Media is the publishing house of the Daughters of St. Paul, an international congregation of women religious serving the Church with the communications media.

1 2 3 4 5 6 7 8 9   25 24 23 22 21

To my daughter,
the real Sara Quinn.

Thank you for
helping me see God.

Sara Quinn was a little girl with big faith. She believed in guardian angels ever since the day her mother said: "God gave every boy and every girl a guardian angel."

Sara Quinn often imagined what her angel looked like. She once drew a picture of an angel three times her size with wings as big as sails.

Because of her faith, God allowed her
guardian angel to deliver a special message in
a special way.

One ordinary morning when Sara Quinn was getting ready for school, the most extraordinary thing happened.

"Hello, Sara Quinn. I am your guardian angel," the angel said as she quietly appeared before her. "God has allowed me to show you something that angels can see. Would you like that?"

The guardian angel laid her hand on Sara Quinn's shoulder and—without a word—she began to see the world as her guardian angel did.

And wow, the world was different! There were angels and bright lights everywhere.

Sara Quinn went to school that day and was delighted to see that her mother was right. There was an angel for every person.

That night when Sara Quinn and her mother said their bedtime prayers, the most amazing thing happened.

"Dear God," Sara Quinn whispered. "I pray for Grandpa's soul, that you take him safely and quickly into heaven."

When they prayed for Grandpa, a glittering light surrounded them. She noticed her guardian angel again.

She gathered up all the prayers into a bowl. She gave Sara Quinn a wink and whisked away into the night. This made Sara Quinn happy. She was sure her angel would bring her prayers straight to God.

Outside the window, Sara Quinn was
surprised to see similar shiny prayers being
carried to God from other houses on her street.
All the guardian angels followed the light
stretching into the sky.

Sara Quinn slept well that night. She knew
her guardian angel was with her.

On Sunday morning, Sara Quinn's family got ready for Mass. It was hectic as ever.

There are so many angels to see, thought Sara Quinn as she slowly got ready. *I don't want to go to church for boring Mass.*

"Sara Quinn, don't make me ask again. Put your shoes and socks on and come downstairs," said her mom.

On the drive to church, Sara Quinn saw more amazing things. Guardian angels carrying prayers almost filled the sky! She also saw a beam of light.

I wonder why there are so many more prayers on Sunday mornings, thought Sara Quinn. *And where is the ray of light coming from?*

Sara Quinn wanted to solve this mystery
instead of going to church.

To her delight, however, they were driving
toward the heavenly light.

"Hey! That's coming from our church!"
exclaimed Sara Quinn.

"What's coming from our church, Honey?" her mom asked puzzled.

"Ummm, nothing, Mom. It's just such a beautiful day," Sara said quickly, realizing that only she could see what her guardian angel saw.

   Shining straight up in the sky like a miracle
spotlight was a sparkling beam that seemed to
stretch all the way to heaven. As she walked into
church, Sara Quinn noticed the beam of light was
coming from a gold box at the front of the church.
   "What is that?" Sara Quinn asked in
amazement.
   "That's called a tabernacle," her mother
answered. "It's where Jesus lives."
   I know that, thought Sara Quinn. *What I don't
know is why the miracle spotlight is shining on the
tabernacle.*

That day Mass was more like a birthday party than a boring time to be quiet. Sara Quinn saw all kinds of angels and saints. They were singing and bowing along with everybody else.

When it came time for the priest to consecrate the bread and the wine, the light from the altar was almost blinding. And then she saw why.

"It's Jesus!" Sara Quinn gasped.

"Yes, Honey," her mom said surprised. "Jesus is fully present in the Eucharist: body, blood, soul, and divinity. That means God is right there on the altar; it's like a little glimpse of heaven for us."

Her mom was even more surprised, however, when Sara Quinn responded, "And he's got such a nice smile!" Sara Quinn's mother raised her eyebrows slightly, but then smiled and whispered, "I'm sure he does, Sweetie."

Sara Quinn wasn't sure her mother quite understood, but she didn't have time to puzzle over that for long. When it came time for her to receive a blessing from the priest and for her mother to receive Communion, the most spectacular thing happened! The priest held out what looked like the most dazzling circle of bread for her mother. And as she ate it, her entire body began to glow!

"You're so lucky, Mom, that you've already made your first Communion," Sara Quinn said as they returned to the pew. She noticed that everyone who had received Communion was glowing.

"Don't forget you have your first Communion this year, Honey," her mother whispered with a smile.

That's right. My first Communion! Sara Quinn thought excitedly. *Now I understand.*

When Mass was over, Sara Quinn turned to her
guardian angel and asked, "Are you showing me all of
this because I am preparing for my first Communion?
Is this supposed to help me understand what really
happens at Mass and when I pray?"

"Yes! God wanted you to have this special gift," she
responded kindly, "so that your faith could grow."

"Thank you!" Sara Quinn replied. "I will always remember this."

"I'll be right here beside you, Sara Quinn," said her guardian angel, "even if you cannot see me. Remember how powerful your prayers are, and that Jesus is always with you too. He can't wait until the day you make your first Communion."

And with that, her guardian angel vanished from her sight. From that moment on, Sara Quinn could no longer see her guardian angel or the shining light, but she remembered everything, and she knew in her heart that she was not alone.

And neither are you. Your guardian angel is always beside you, and Jesus waits for you at every Mass!

Angel of God

Angel of God, my guardian dear, to whom God's love entrusts me here; ever this day, be at my side, to light and guard, to rule and guide. Amen.

Prayer of Thanksgiving
for the Eucharist

Dear Jesus,

I am so happy to be here with you, really present in the Eucharist. I love you and I want to live each day as your friend. Thank you for the gift of my guardian angel and for the friendship of all the angels and saints, especially of your mother Mary, who is also my heavenly mother. Please take care of _____ [tell Jesus about any people or things you would like to pray for]. Thank you for loving me and for always hearing my prayers. Amen.

PARENTS CORNER

"Take care that you do not despise one of these little ones; for, I tell you, in heaven their angels continually see the face of my Father" (Matthew 18:10).

Gravity. Space. Time. These are all constants in the universe that cannot be seen. What would each of these look like if we could see them? This story is to help children understand the unseen spiritual realities of our universe.

Catholics believe that an angel stands beside every person as protector and shepherd leading them to salvation.

Angels are often depicted as messengers in the Bible. In the Gospel of Luke, for example, we can read about the Archangel Gabriel who announced to Mary that she would be the mother of Jesus (Luke 1: 26–38).

Catholics also believe in the communion of saints. Every person who dies in a state of grace is promised heaven, though they may go to purgatory first to be prepared. This is why we pray for those who have died.

When we pray to Our Lady and the angels and saints, we trust them to bring our prayers to God. At Mass, we join the entire communion of saints and the faithful around the world in praising and worshipping God.

Receiving Jesus in holy Communion is the greatest gift that God has given us!

Jesus said, "This is the bread that came down from heaven. Unlike your ancestors who ate and still died, whoever eats this bread will live forever" (John 6:58).

At the Last Supper, Jesus commanded: "This is my body, which will be given for you; do this in memory of me" (Luke 22:19). And the last thing Jesus promised was: "And behold, I am with you always, until the end of the age" (Matthew 28:20).

Matthew Kilmurry

I first wrote *What Angels See* when my oldest daughter, Sara Quinn, was preparing for the Sacrament of Holy Communion. I scratched the words on a notebook and illustrated them with stick figures. I wanted to show her the amazing spiritual world alive all around us, most especially in the Eucharist, that our eyes can't see but our hearts can feel if we only let them. I would dust off the notebook and read the story again with each new child.

I now have eight children, three of whom have yet to read the story. I hope this book fires your imagination, as it did theirs, and opens the door of your heart to your guardian angel, the saints in heaven, and most especially our Lord Jesus Christ.

Parents: Looking to inspire your faith? Check out my other book, *You Are the Catholic Brand,* from Liguori Publications.

Tammie Lyon

Tammie Lyon is an award-winning author and illustrator of numerous books for children. She is known for her work on the *Eloise* series for Simon and Schuster as well as for the wildly popular *Katie Woo* series. With over one million copies sold, Capstone Publishing has decided to launch two new spin-off series, *Pedro: First Grade Hero* and *Katie and Pedro Mysteries,* based on Katie's friend, which Tammie is hard at work on.

Tammie has illustrated numerous books for children, creating work for Disney, Scholastic, Simon and Schuster, Penguin, HarperCollins, and Amazon Publishing to name a few. She has turned to writing and illustrating her own titles as well. Her first picture book, *Olive and Snowflake,* was released to starred reviews from Kirkus and School Library Journal.

Tammie lives in Cincinnati, Ohio, with her husband, Lee, and two dogs, Amos and Artie. She spends her days writing and drawing in her home studio in the woods surrounded by wildlife and, of course, two mostly always sleeping dogs.

Tales and Legends from

Pauline kids

The 3 Trees
Adapted by Gabriel Ringlet
Illustrated by Daniella Oh

The Little Lost Lamb
Written and Illustrated by Ceci Berger Haines

the QUEEN & the CROSS
The Story of Saint Helen
Written by Cornelia Mary Bilinsky
Illustrated by Rebecca Stuhff

Spider's Gift
A Christmas Story
Written by Geraldine Ada Marshall
Illustrated by Rebecca Sorge

The Saint Who Fought the Dragon
The Story of Saint George
Written by Cornelia Mary Bilinsky
Illustrated by Theresa Brandon

SANTA'S Secret Story
Written by Cornelia Mary Bilinsky
Illustrated by Candace Camling

34

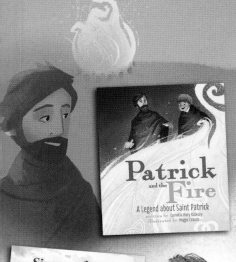

Patrick and the Fire
A Legend about Saint Patrick
written by Cornelia Mary Bilinsky
illustrated by Maggie Coburn

A Legend about Saint Brigid of Ireland
Brigid and the Butter

Simon of Cyrene
and the Legend of the Easter Egg
Written by Terri DeGezelle
Illustrated by Gabhor Utomo

Brother Lorenzo's Pretzels
Prayer and the Holy Trinity
Includes Recipe!
Written by Cornelia Mary Bilinsky
Illustrated by John Joseph

A Prayer and a Pickaxe
A LEGEND ABOUT ST. CLEMENT OF ROME
WRITTEN BY PAMELA LOVE   ILLUSTRATED BY MAGGIE COBURN

A Story of Prayer and Saint Joseph
Staircase for the Sisters
written by Pamela Love   illustrated by John Joseph

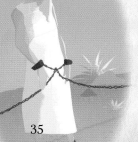

35

THE LEGEND OF THE FIRST VALENTINE
A STORY OF GOD'S LOVE
WRITTEN BY CORNELIA BILINSKY
ILLUSTRATED BY ANDREA TRIPKE

Who are the Daughters of St. Paul?

We are Catholic sisters with a mission. Our task is to bring the love of Jesus to everyone like Saint Paul did. You can find us in over 50 countries. Our founder, Blessed James Alberione, showed us how to reach out to the world through the media. That's why we publish books, make movies and apps, record music, broadcast on radio, perform concerts, help people at our bookstores, visit parishes, host JClub book fairs, use social media and the Internet, and pray for all of you.

Pauline
BOOKS & MEDIA

The Daughters of St. Paul operate book and media centers at the following addresses. Visit, call, or write the one nearest you today, or find us at www.paulinestore.org.

CALIFORNIA
3908 Sepulveda Blvd, Culver City, CA 90230   310-397-8676
3250 Middlefield Road, Menlo Park, CA 94025   650-562-7060

FLORIDA
145 SW 107th Avenue, Miami, FL 33174   305-559-6715

HAWAII
1143 Bishop Street, Honolulu, HI 96813   808-521-2731

ILLINOIS
172 North Michigan Avenue, Chicago, IL 60601   312-346-4228

LOUISIANA
4403 Veterans Memorial Blvd, Metairie, LA 70006   504-887-7631

MASSACHUSETTS
885 Providence Hwy, Dedham, MA 02026   781-326-5385

MISSOURI
9804 Watson Road, St. Louis, MO 63126   314-965-3512

NEW YORK
115 E. 29th Street, New York City, NY 10016   212-754-1110

SOUTH CAROLINA
243 King Street, Charleston, SC 29401   843-577-0175

VIRGINIA
1025 King Street, Alexandria, VA 22314   703-549-3806

CANADA
3022 Dufferin Street, Toronto, ON M6B 3T5   416-781-9131